# FOREWORD

A land of myth and mystery, its past steeped in the triumph and tragedy of a timeless struggle for freedom. The realm of warrior poets, when its people are subdued they turn to the legends of history for nourishment as it is the deeds of heroes that bring solace in the darkest times.

Centuries ago it was considered the "End of the World", where all journeys cease. Now a new journey begins.

The Immortal Guardian brings epic storytelling and breathtaking artwork to an ancient narrative within the modern comic book medium, a universal tale of the enduring fight against persecution and a saviour created to defend his people in the face of insurmountable odds.

As chaos reigns, the immortal guardian awakens.

**"Those who do not move do not notice their chains."**

# CHAPTER 1

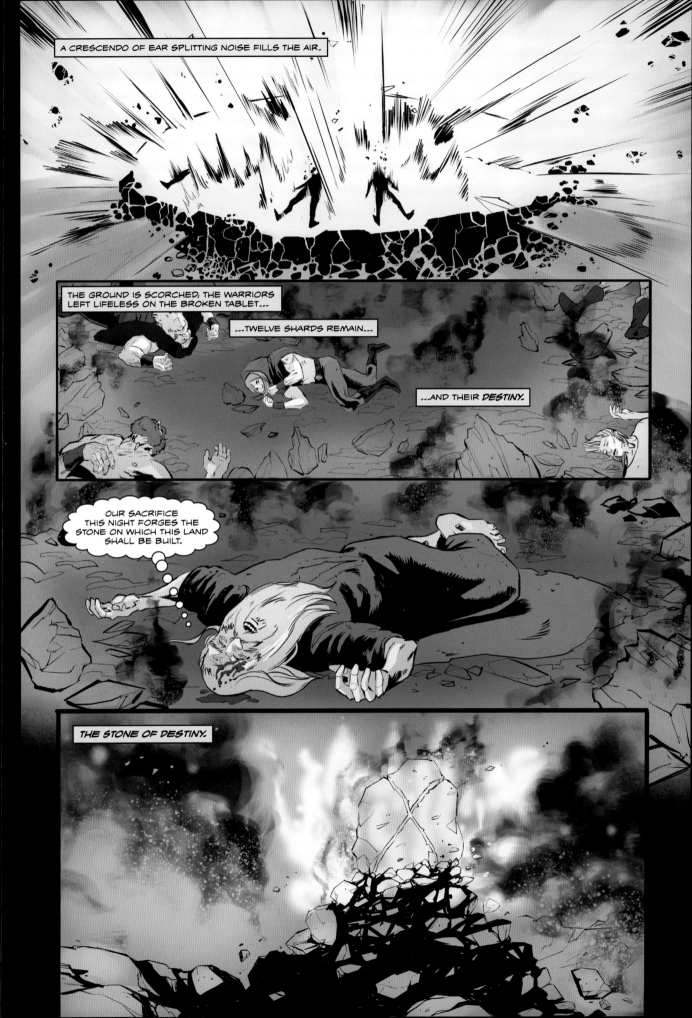

A FIGURE REMAINS...

...THE ETERNAL CREATION.

THE IMMORTAL GUARDIAN AWAKENS.

# SALTIRE

SCRIPT: JOHN FERGUSON    ART: CLAIRE ROE, TONE JULSKJAER & GARY WELSH
COLOURS: LAUREN KNIGHT    LETTERS: PHILLIP VAUGHAN

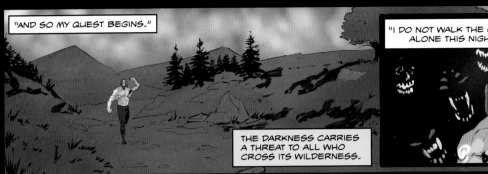

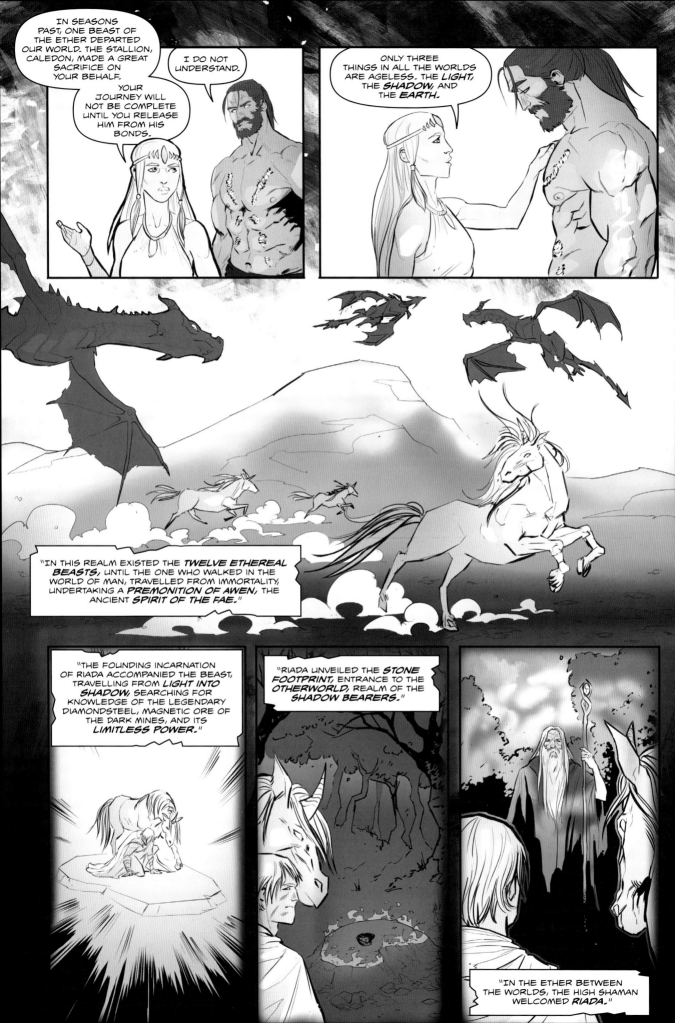

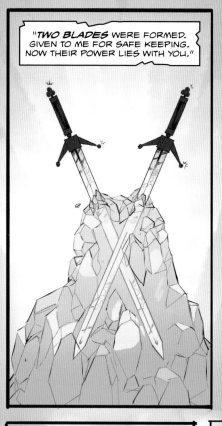

"*TWO BLADES* WERE FORMED. GIVEN TO ME FOR SAFE KEEPING. NOW THEIR POWER LIES WITH YOU."

"*CALEDON*, OVER THE CYCLES OF THE MOON, DESCENDED INTO SHADOW, GLEANING THE POWER OF THE OTHERWORLD, LEFT WITH ONLY A GLIMMER OF ETHEREAL LIGHT."

I BID YOU FAREWELL. MAY THE BLUE STONE GUIDE YOU THROUGH THE STORMS OF THE MORTAL WORLD.

WILL I SEE YOU AGAIN?

I CANNOT RETURN IF EVER I LEAVE THIS REALM. I WOULD CLAIM THE FATE OF A MORTAL.

MY PRESENCE WILL ALWAYS BE WITH YOU. LOOK TO THE STARS WHEN DARKNESS AND DESPAIR HAVE OVERCOME. THE NORTHERN LIGHTS ARE OF THIS REALM. THEY WILL HEAL YOU IN THE BLACKEST OF NIGHTS.

BEAUTY FILLS THE NIGHT SKY. THE LIGHT OF THE FAE.

ADD – ANCIENT FOOTPRINT OF THE SHADOW BEARERS.

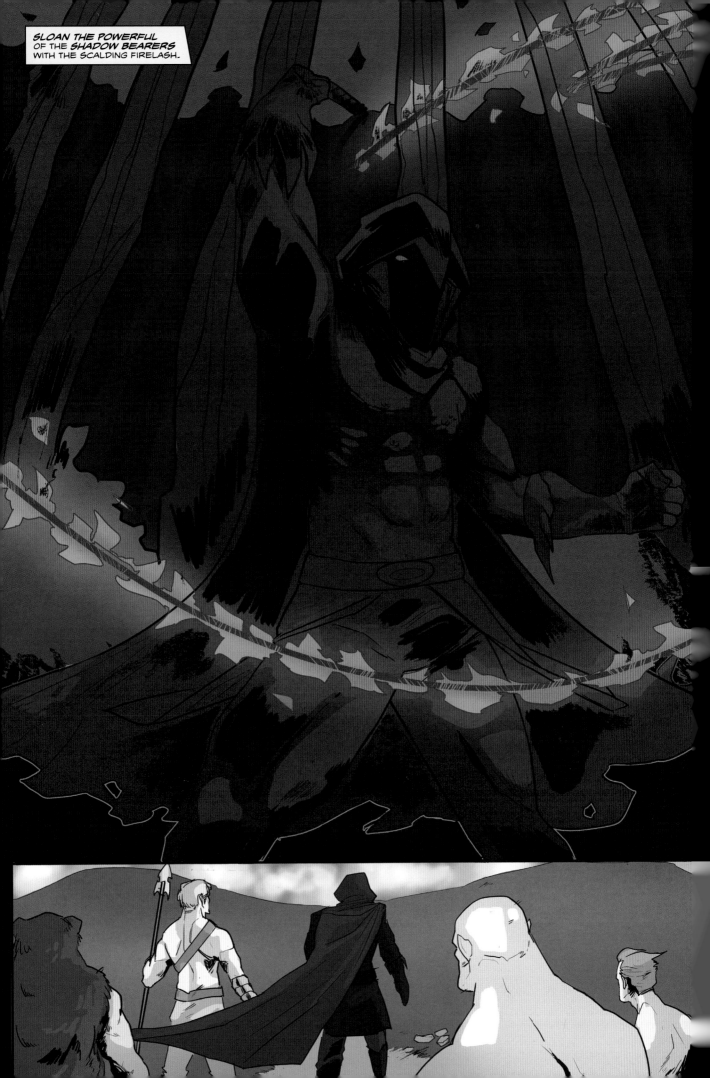

SLOAN THE POWERFUL OF THE *SHADOW BEARERS* WITH THE SCALDING FIRELASH.

THE STONE OF DESTINY. FORGED ON THE MOUNTAIN OF ETHER BY THE SPIRITS OF THE TWELVE CLANS.

THE BALANCE OF *LIGHT AND SHADOW* CALLS UPON THE *THIRTEENTH TRIBE.*

THE *ULTIMATE GUARDIAN* IS SUMMONED...

THE NINTH LEGION STANDS AS ONE.

THEY HAVE AMASSED A SMALL FORCE GENERAL. THEY ARE *EXPECTING* US!

WE ATTACK AT FIRST LIGHT!

HE AWAITS THE *ROMAN ARMY.*

*THE IMMORTAL PROTECTOR,* THE EMBODIMENT OF HIS PEOPLE.

THE COUNTRY IS AT PEACE ONCE MORE.

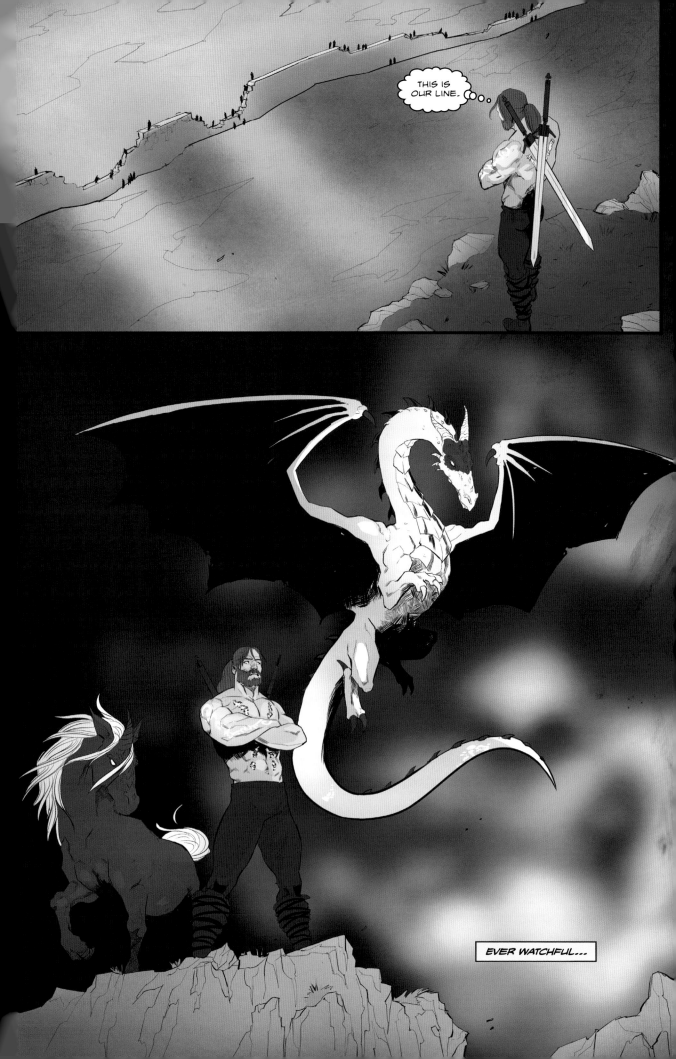

CHAPTER 2

HE CAVES OF THE NESS...

...SALTIRE LOOKS TO THE HIGH SHAMAN, *MORMAER.*

THE GUARDIANS HAVE CONTROLLED THE INTRUSIONS SO FAR. BUT THE THREAT OF THE MERCYAN HANGS OVER US.

DO NOT TROUBLE YOURSELF. REST A WHILE.

NATHIR AND CALEDON - THE BEASTS OF POWER AND WISDOM.

MY CONCERN LIES WITH OUR COUNTRY. THE POWER OF THE SHAMAN WILL RISE ONCE MORE.

IT MAKES IT NO EASIER TO SEE YOU SO WEAK.

PREPARE YOURSELF. THIS MENACE IS UNLIKE ANY WE HAVE SEEN. THE IMMORTALS CAN BRING HOPE IN OUR HOUR OF NEED. EILYS MAY NOT WALK IN OUR WORLD BUT SHE HAS THE POWER TO SAVE IT.

THE MORTAL WORLD IS IN PERIL.

A DANGEROUS COUNTENANCE THREATENS THE CLANS.

WE ARE EXPECTANT OF WAR. THE SAXON INTENTIONS ARE CLEAR.

BE MINDFUL, THIS TERROR IS RELENTLESS. THEY CARRY A POWERFUL SORCERY. THEIR ONE INTENTION.... *DESTRUCTION.*

GUARDIA – SAXON STRONGHOLD.
THESE BARBAROUS FOOLS, SO ARROGANT THEY FORGET TO PROTECT THEMSELVES.
BRING ME MORE WINE, NOW!
A KING MAY NEED HIS WITS ABOUT HIM WHEN HE RECEIVES VISITORS.
YOUR IMPUDENCE WILL BE...
MY LADY. I DID NOT SEE YOU IN THE DARKNESS.
AS WAS MY INTENTION.
I WISH TO PURCHASE YOUR TALENTS.
MY TALENTS ARE NOT FOR SALE!
I CAN MAKE YOU RICH BEYOND MEASURE.
ANYTHING YOU DREAM OF COULD BE YOURS. I ASK ONLY YOU DISTRACT THOSE WHO BLIGHT OUR EXPANSION TO THE NORTH.
THE GLINT OF GOLD DOES NOTHING FOR ME. MY DREAMS FLOW WITH CRIMSON.

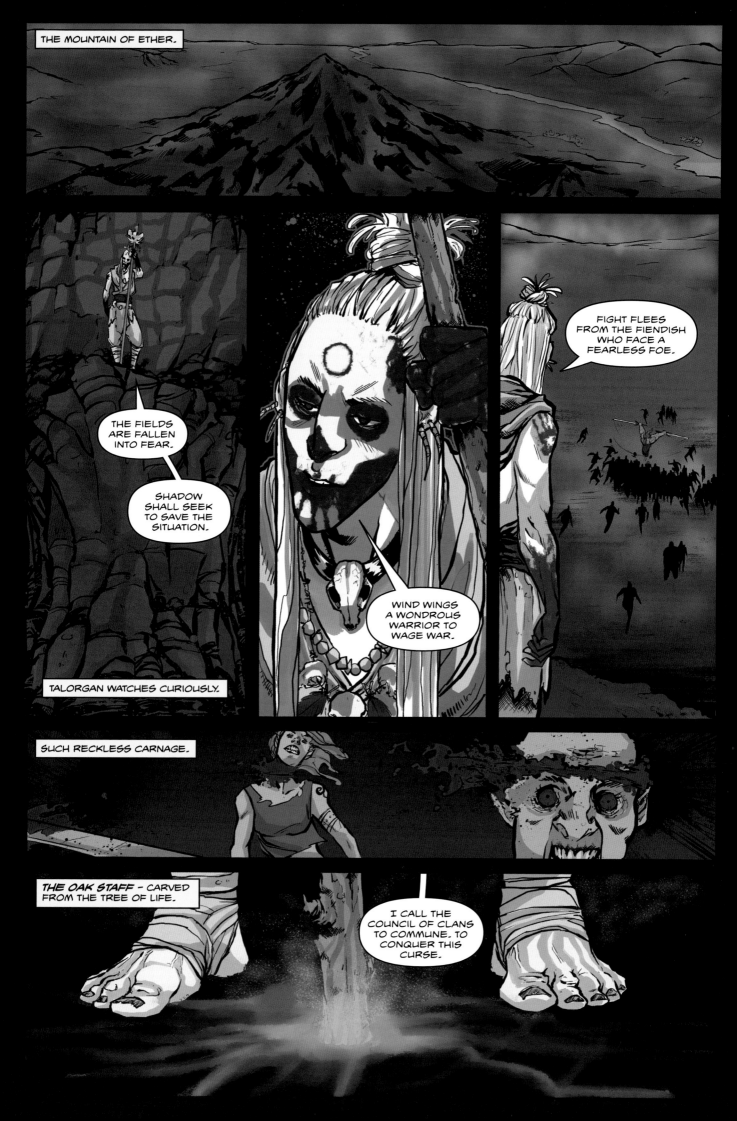

SING LITTLE SISTER, SING.

...BLOOD COMES OUT SO NO ONE KNOWS.

HELMET OF THE MERCYAN PROTECT ME.

HMM...

HMMM!

IT TINGLES.

WHAT IN THE WORLDS...!

HOOOWWWLII!!!

THANK YOU MY BROTHER.

NOOOOOO!!!

THE BLOOD OF A GUARDIAN, AAH!

I AM SORRY. KILL ME...

...YOU MUST.

KILL ME!

AAH!

THE SPECTRE OF DEATH UPON THE GUARDIANS.

YOU TEMPT ME FURTHER.

BRODE? NO... YOU ARE ONE OF US.

YOU DO NOT UNDERSTAND THE POWER OF THE THIRST.

ONLY BLOOD CAN QUENCH MY HUNGER.

DESIRE OF THE UNDEAD.

DO NOT FEEL SYMPATHY. THEY WILL HAVE NO MERCY FOR YOU.

**CHAPTER 3**

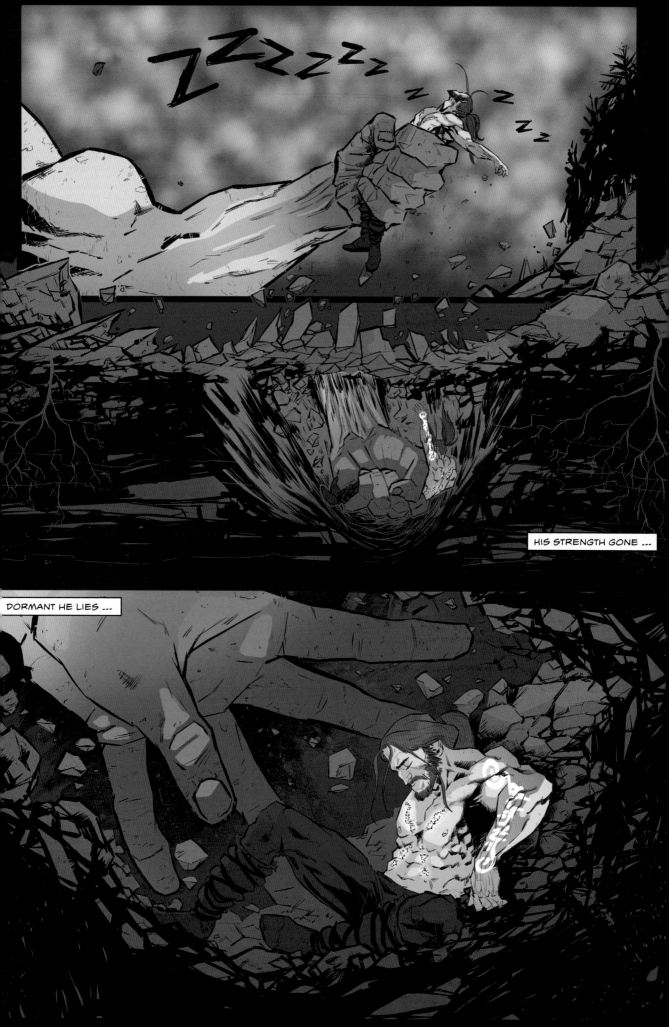

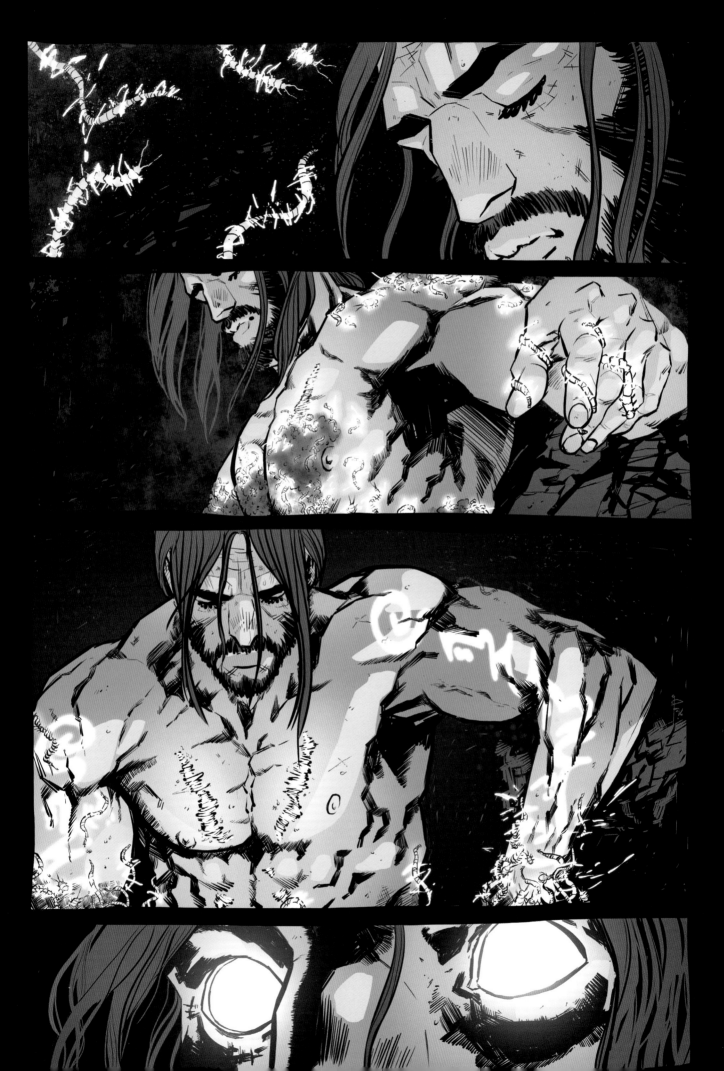

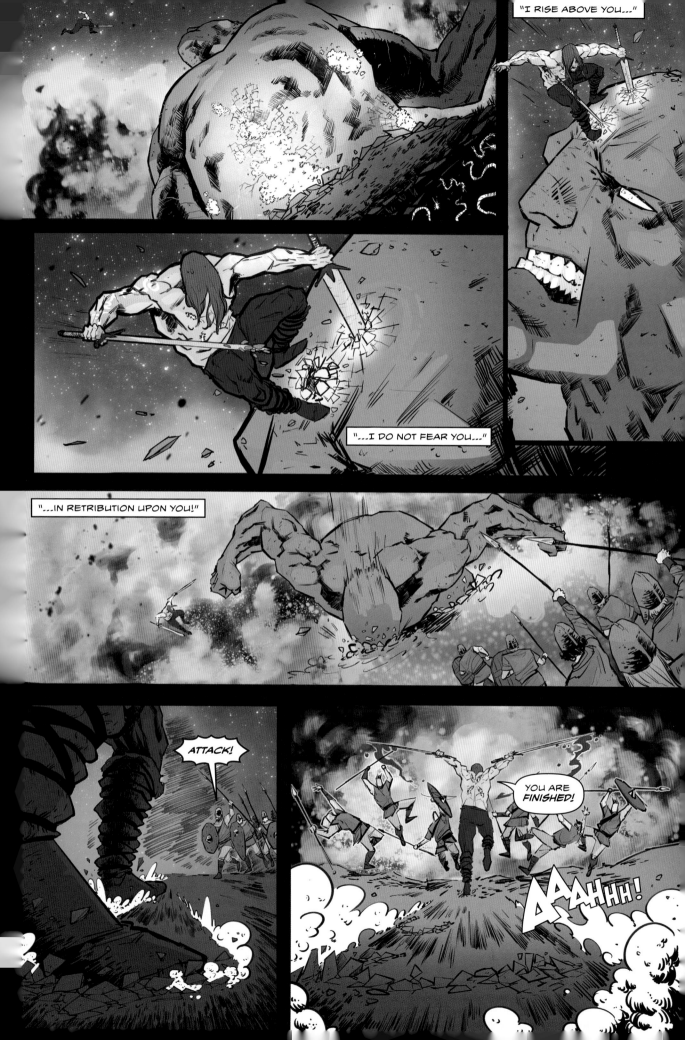

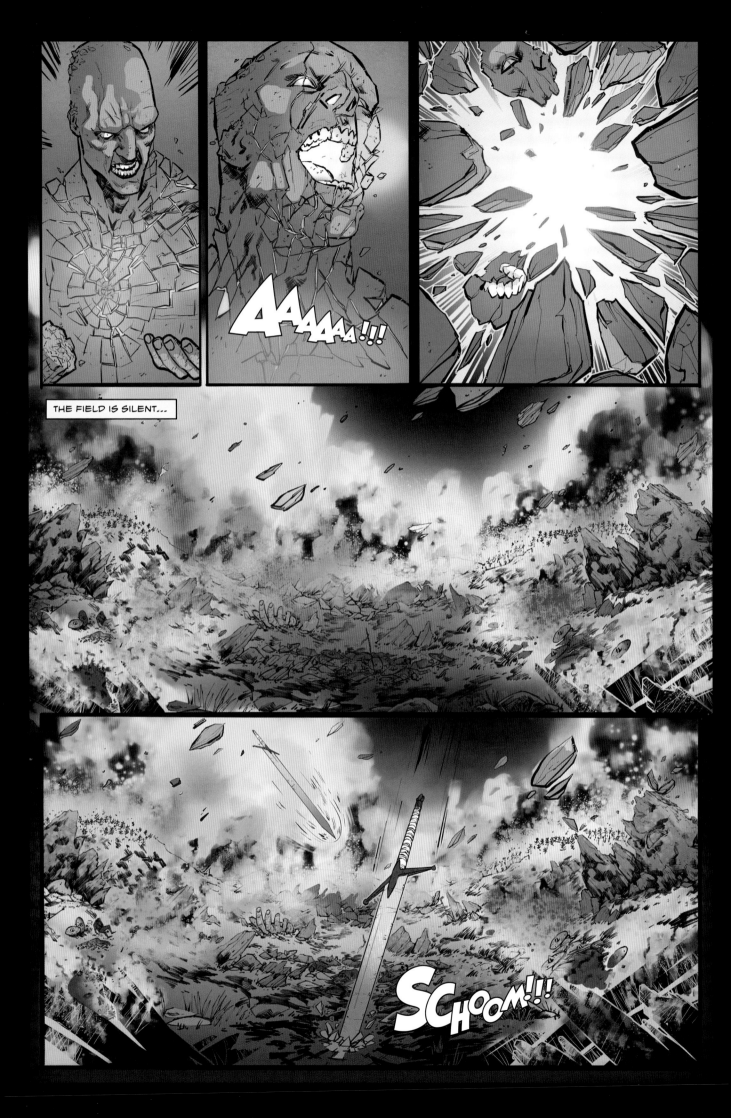

A LAND OF THE FREE.